Sally Kindberg's
DRAW IT!

CHRISTMAS

BLOOMSBURY
Activity Books

Draw a Christmas meal made up of five things you can see in front of you.

Draw the front page of the North Pole News.

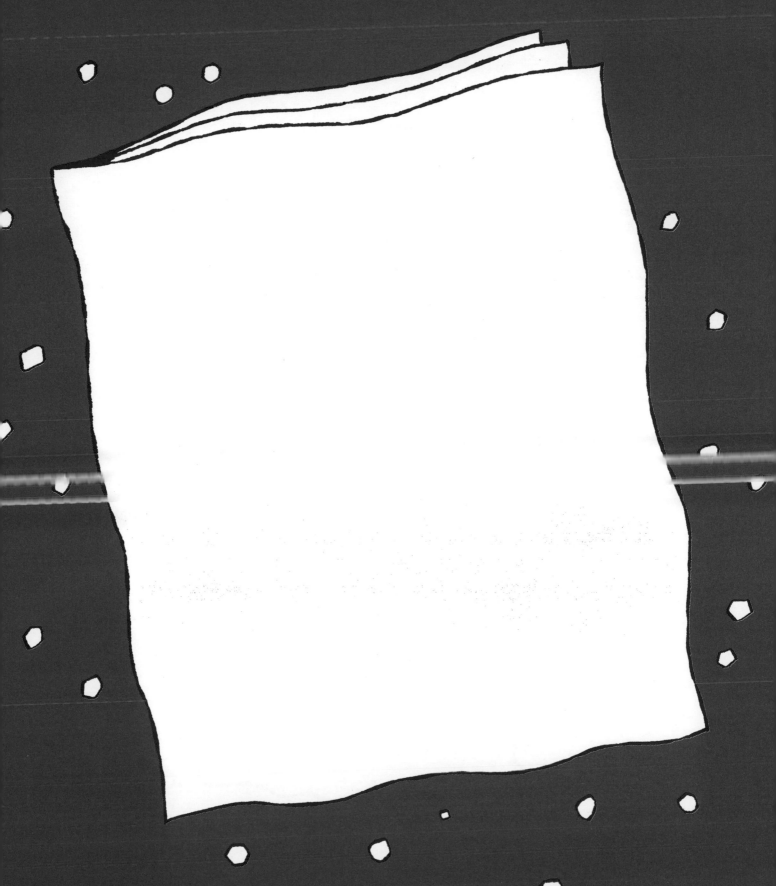

Draw outfits for these snowmen.

Quick, before they melt!

Draw some Christmas sounds:

Jingle.

Ding.

Crackle.

Make this
elf look
cheerful.

Draw a grumpy
face on this
brussel sprout.

Draw what's inside these Christmas parcels. Who would you send them to?

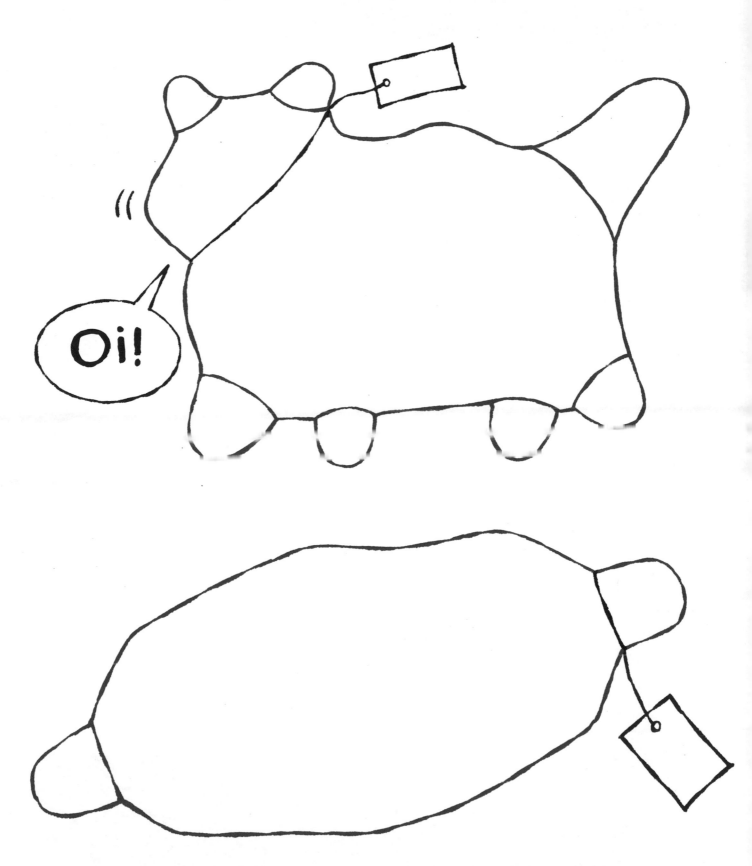

Family not up to scratch this Christmas? Draw your ideal family.

SWAP...
Two boring
brothers for
one eccentric
cousin?

There are mysterious
footprints in the
snow outside.

Who do they belong to? Draw it!

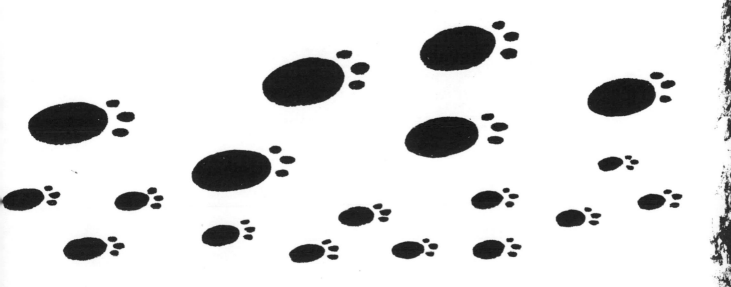

Draw a map of Santa's journey from the North Pole to your house.

Draw some
Christmas
words:

Joy.

Snuggle.

Hug.

Draw Santa's designer pyjamas and slippers.

Draw some North Pole sounds:

Scrunch
of snow.

Howl of the wind.

Creak of ice.

Draw splash.

Draw these presents:

a tin of happiness,

a bag of nasty (tee hee)

and a box of surprise.

Draw a Christmas monster having fun.

Chatter!
Chatter!

Draw cold.

There's lots of magic
about at Christmas.

What goes on inside your freezer? Draw it.

Santa decides to get fit for Christmas. Draw a comic strip to show what happens next.

Draw another Christmas comic strip here.

Draw a SUPERSLEDGE.

How's it powered?

What's it made of?

Can it fly?

How fast can it go?

Draw your favourite Christmas food on this table.

If you could invite anyone at all for Christmas lunch, who would you invite?

* Happy Christmas

Draw Santa's favourite pastime when he's not delivering presents.

Invent and draw a special Christmas constellation (a pattern made up of stars).

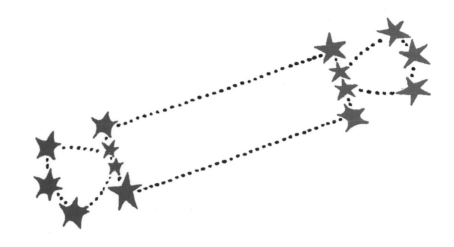

Low fat

Draw some
treats for Santa.

Draw a surprise
Christmas visitor
(no, not Santa).

Morning! Jack Frost's the name

Don't know how
to draw a snowman?
Draw a festive Stickman.

Or a Recycleman.

Draw six uses for holly leaves, including something really unpleasant (if you must).

Draw the best Christmas present you've ever been given.

Draw a Christmas ghost family. Where do they live?

Wooo!

Draw a spaceship from another galaxy come to investigate Earthling Christmas.

Your great-great-great-granddad travels by time machine to arrive for Christmas dinner. Draw it.

You use your time machine to visit Christmas in the past or future. Where do you go? Draw it.

Give Santa a makeover.

Before

After

Draw the worst
Christmas present
you can imagine.

Draw the character
you'd like to be in a
Christmas play.

You're going to
a fancy dress
Christmas party.
Draw it!

Draw your favourite Christmas party game.

The Wobble Like A Jelly Game

Draw who you would definitely not invite for Christmas dinner.

Draw Santa on his summer holiday.

A rebus is a message
that uses pictures as
well as letters of the
alphabet to make words.

 you t 🏺

this in 2

a rebus?

SEE YOU LATER.
I HAVE GONE TO
FIND A REINDEER.

Draw six uses for an old Christmas pudding (apart from eating it).

Draw the worst
Christmas joke
you've ever heard.

Invent and draw a special SatNav for Santa (SantaNav?)

Draw a joke-testing machine for a Christmas cracker factory.

jokes

It's Christmas time on the pirate ship The Nasty Ned.

Draw what
happens.

(not TOO gory please).

Draw a character from your favourite Christmas song.

Draw some wild creatures living in this Christmas tree.

What's the best thing you've ever found in a cracker? Draw it!

What's the worst thing you've ever found in a cracker? Draw it!

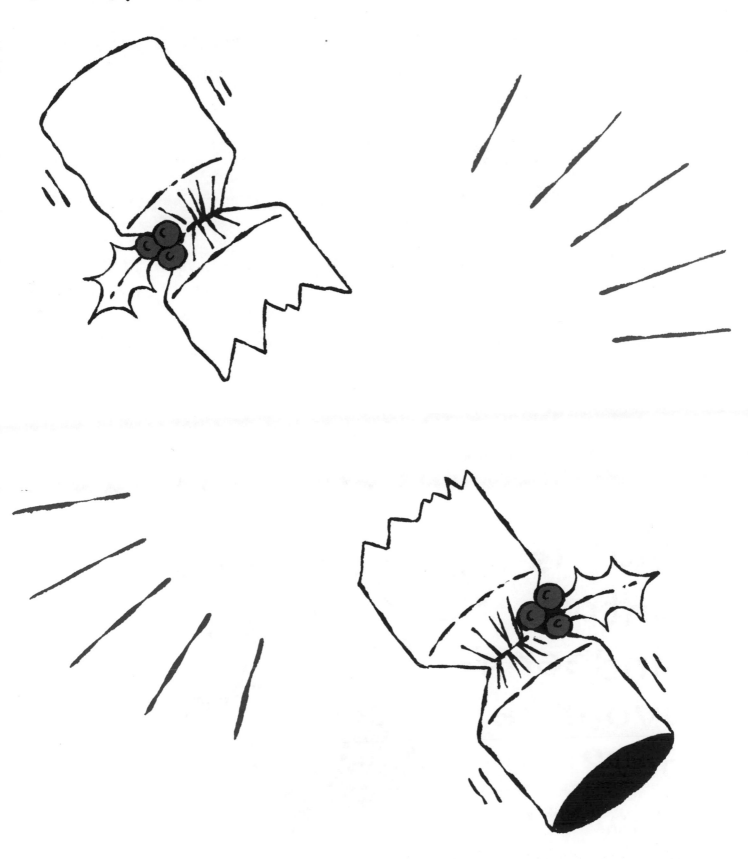

What is Santa's reindeer's favourite food? Draw it!

Draw what you would give a witch for Christmas.

What would you
give a giant for
Christmas?
Draw it!

Draw what
you would give
a zombie for
Christmas.

Draw what you would give Dracula for Christmas.

Draw an outfit that's
just right for the
North Pole.

Invent and draw some Christmas decorations made from:

Bells

Robins

Frozen noses

Gloves

Icicles

 and/or elves.

Draw how you would travel
to the North Pole.

You're fed up that it's not Christmas yet, and you're in a bad mood.
Draw it.

Bad mood

It's Christmas time on Planet Zblg.
Draw some Zblgians.

Planet
Zblg

Zblgian Christmas
Pudding

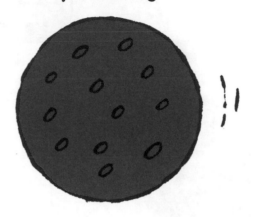

Draw Santa
stuck in this
chimney.

One of your uncles is an explorer. What would you send him for Christmas (if you had his address)? Draw it.

Draw a Christmas present made from some balloons, an old woolly hat and two spare bicycle wheels.

The reindeer have gone on strike and Santa has to leave his sledge back at the North Pole. How does he travel?

Draw a machine for rescuing Santa.

It's Christmas time under the sea. Draw a Seahorse Parade, Best Fin Competition and a Seaweedathon.

The weather's not
very Christmassy.
Draw a Snow Machine.

Oops, it's gone into
Blizzard Mode! Draw it.

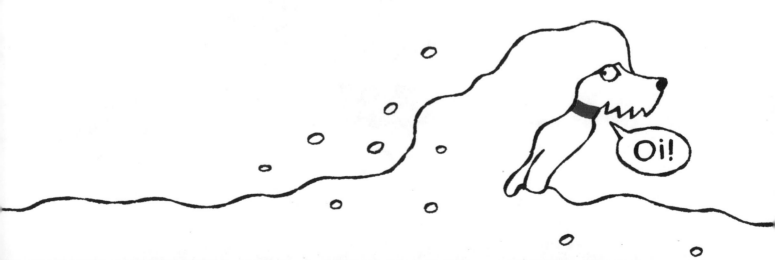

The Grumposauruses find it hard to enjoy Christmas. Draw something to cheer them up.

Draw the best
Christmas
joke you've
ever heard.

Draw something which would make you wake up early enough to open your Christmas presents.

Draw some cheeky Christmas elves.

Draw Santa's
favourite TV
programme.

Your cousin practises a magic trick at Christmas, but he turns your aunt into a...draw it!

Draw some strange
creatures in this
Christmas grotto.

You're given a
magical power
for Christmas.
Draw it!

Design a new
sack for Santa.

Draw a giant evil snowball chasing people down a hill.

How could you stop the snowball from squashing everyone? Draw it.

Draw some little-known
Christmas sports:
Cracker Hurling.

The Two-legged Sock Jump Race.

You will need a large sock.

The Badly Wrapped Parcel Hurdles.

Draw a prize for the Christmas Sports.

← ICE CREAM

FIRST PRIZE

Who would you choose to give the prize to?

Disqualified (4 feet)

You have lost your Christmas holiday homework. Draw the excuse you're going to give your teacher.

Draw a
parcel
wrapping
machine.

It's Christmas Eve, the stars are twinkling, but what else can you see in the sky?

One of your Christmas presents is a robot. What would you programme it to do?

The robot isn't taking orders... in fact, it has decided to do exactly the opposite! Draw what happens next.

It's late, you're sleepy and it begins to snow heavily... Draw an unusual way of getting home safely to your warm bed.